£4.75

"RECIPE FOR DISASTER"

I'VE GOT BAD NEWS AND GOOD NEWS . . .

I LOVE READING "THE BEANO".

GOOD AT COOKING? I THOUGHT TEACHER SAID "WHO'S GOOD-LOOKING"?

WE DIDN'T KNOW YOU WERE GOOD-LOOKING EITHER.

READ THE RECIPE, SMIFFY. PEEL ONIONS, WILFRID. FATTY . . .

WAIT! I'VE GOT A JOB ALREADY.

DONK!

ONIONS

I'M THE FOOD TASTER!

FIRST AID LADY — QUICK!

YIKES! WE'VE GOT TO GET HIM OUT OF HERE!

S·O·S

PHEW! HE'S ALL RIGHT.

THANK GOODNESS! I DIDN'T FANCY GIVING HIM THE KISS OF LIFE!

Soon —

. . . TEN TABLESPOONS OF PEPPER — LOTS OF CURRY POWDER — A WHOLE LOAD OF MUSTARD AND . . .

WHO WANTS TO TASTE IT?

I WILL.

TEACHER'S A HERO.

TEACHER'S AN IDIOT!

GLAARGH!

THE CONGA EEL

Of all the creatures in the ocean
None displays such funky motion,
As Conga Eel - a pal of mine
Who does the conga all the time.

When he starts to dance and swim
All the fishes follow him.
Be careful if you join the queue
Lest Conga makes a meal of you!

My first day at School

My parents were upset at leaving me.

'BYE, SON!

BE A GOOD LAD!

DOG POUND

SCHOOL

PAT!

The classrooms were small.

NNGH!

But my classmates were very friendly.

I must have been in the wrong class.

SHRIEK! A CHILD!

But eventually I found my way to Bash Street School.

'ERBERT

GLOBAL WARRING

Geography class—

WHERE'S ANNAPURNA?

THIS BIT . . .

THAT BIT THERE . . .

THEY'RE STUDYING.

WE'VE STUDIED AND WE'VE MADE SOMETHING OF IT, TEACHER.

GOOD-GOOD! WHAT?

EEK!

WHERE'S HE GONE?

AAIIIEEEE . . .

. . . AAH!

GRR! ILL-TREATING SCHOOL EQUIPMENT AGAIN — ROPES ARE FOR CLIMBING — NOT . . .

. . . TRAMPOLINES ARE NOT FOR NAPS — THEY'RE FOR BOUNCING . . .

PUSH!

. . . LIKE THIS— SNIGGER!

BOING!

SHE'S NOT HERE — TOOTS IS THE ONLY GIRL IN THIS CLASS! MAYBE ANNA'S IN SOME OTHER CLASS.

IF EVER A TEACHER SUFFERED.

ANNAPURNA IS NOT A GIRL — IT'S A MOUNTAIN IN THE HIMALAYAS — AND YOU LOT ARE ABSOLUTELY HOPELESS AT GEOGRAPHY!

WOW! YOU LEARN SOMETHING NEW EVERY DAY.

STUDY THIS AND SEE WHAT YOU CAN MAKE OF IT.

DOOF!

ASHING TBALL!

GIVE ME THAT — AND KINDLY STOP ILL-TREATING SCHOOL EQUIPMENT!

NICE SAVE.

EVERYONE DOWN TO THE GYM FOR P. E. — BEFORE I LOSE MY TEMPER!

DRING! TRING!

ROPE CLIMBING, BEGIN. YOU FIRST, PLUG!

SWINGING! OUCH!

THUD!

WHUMP!

M-MORE ILL-TREATMENT OF SCHOOL EQUIPMENT . . .

SNORE!

HOWL!

Later—

WE'VE ALL GOT 500 LINES— "I MUST NOT ILL-TREAT SCHOOL EQUIPMENT . . ."

". . . INCLUDING TEACHER!"

MUMBLE!

MOVIE MAYHEM

1 "**M**UMFLE! Umfle! Gerble! Gloop!" said Fatty, his mouth full of biscuits. "What?" retorted the kids, their faces full of crumbs.

"He said, 'Mumfle! Umfle! Gerble! Gloop!' which means 'my pig drinks milk' in a rare dialect of Swahili," said Cuthbert swottily. "Shut up!" said the kids in unison, together and all at once.

2 *Fatty cleared his throat, belched and cleared the room. When the kids filed back in wearing gas masks, Fatty explained, "I said let's go to the pictures!"*

6 *At that moment a snail overtook Teacher's car. "We'd be quicker walking!" said Wilfrid huffily (no-one had spoken to him all day).*

"Agreed!" said Danny, and before you could say "we hate sardines" in nine different languages, everyone got out of the car. Fortunately the car had been parked outside the cinema all along so they didn't have far to walk.

7 *Just as the kids joined the queue, a busker with a bad wig approached them, playing a guitar.*

"That's a very unusual hairpiece!" said Teacher admiringly.

"Hairpiece indeed!" snorted the busker, "that's Malcolm, my trained guinea pig!"

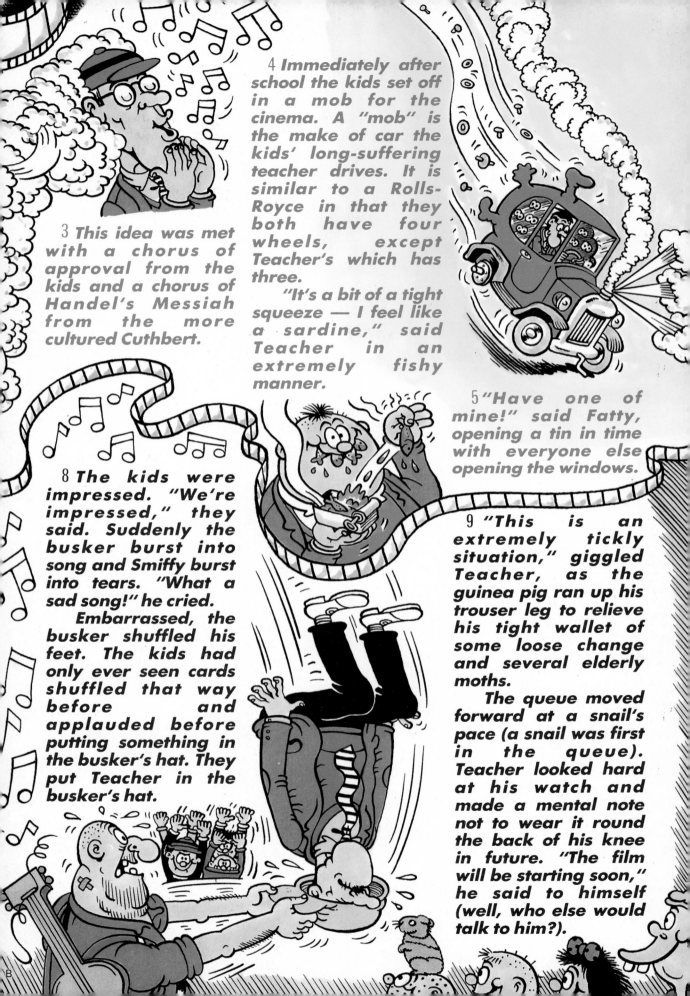

3 This idea was met with a chorus of approval from the kids and a chorus of Handel's Messiah from the more cultured Cuthbert.

4 Immediately after school the kids set off in a mob for the cinema. A "mob" is the make of car the kids' long-suffering teacher drives. It is similar to a Rolls-Royce in that they both have four wheels, except Teacher's which has three.

"It's a bit of a tight squeeze — I feel like a sardine," said Teacher in an extremely fishy manner.

5 "Have one of mine!" said Fatty, opening a tin in time with everyone else opening the windows.

8 The kids were impressed. "We're impressed," they said. Suddenly the busker burst into song and Smiffy burst into tears. "What a sad song!" he cried.

Embarrassed, the busker shuffled his feet. The kids had only ever seen cards shuffled that way before and applauded before putting something in the busker's hat. They put Teacher in the busker's hat.

9 "This is an extremely tickly situation," giggled Teacher, as the guinea pig ran up his trouser leg to relieve his tight wallet of some loose change and several elderly moths.

The queue moved forward at a snail's pace (a snail was first in the queue). Teacher looked hard at his watch and made a mental note not to wear it round the back of his knee in future. "The film will be starting soon," he said to himself (well, who else would talk to him?).

10 "What are we going to see?" asked Toots, in a small voice.

"The Big, Black Stinky Thing from The Horrid Murky Mire!" replied Sidney in a bigger voice.

"What's it about?" 'Erbert asked a lamp-post he had mistaken for Plug.

"School dinners by the sound of it!" said Spotty. They all laughed like they'd never laughed before (it was a noise like a hippo breaking wind in a bagpipe factory).

11 When they arrived in the foyer, Teacher had no choice but to pay for all the kids to get in — they had kidnapped his moustache and were holding it to ransom!

16 Unfortunately, he burst through the cinema screen, totally destroying it. Some of the crowd went mad! After they had been taken away and sedated, Danny had an idea. "I've had an idea!" he said.

Using hairs from Teacher's kidnapped moustache, Danny and the others tied Fatty up so that he stood with his back to the crowd. They left his hands free so that he could continue eating.

15 As his friends' anger rose, Fatty quaked in his shoes then quacked in his shoes as he was forced to duck under a flying blazer thrown by Danny. Cuthbert was still wearing the blazer at the time, which made it doubly dangerous.

Fatty would not be moved — his portly frame having filled out to the point where he was wedged in his seats. Using Teacher's nose as a handy lever, the kids struggled to release Fatty. All of a sudden Fatty popped from his seats with a noise like a fat bloke flying from a chair.

RRIIIP!

12 Once into the cinema, an usherette showed them to their seats with a torch, which was a bit silly really — but she was Smiffy's auntie and no-one had told her the lights were still on. Fatty took up all the seats in the front row, two for his ample behind and the rest for his ample supply of sweets. As the rest of the kids sat down the lights went out and the film started. A triumphant roar echoed round the hall — a lion had sneaked in dressed as a giraffe.

13 "I can't see a thing!" protested 'Erbert, who was the only one with an unrestricted view.

"'Erbert's right!" said Danny, angrily, "I can't see a thing for this tub of lard sitting in front of me!"

14 At that moment Fatty lifted the tub of lard and drained it in one gulp. This was enough to block out the view of Plug, Spotty and Sidney. "We've reached our breaking point!" they snapped.

17 "Okay, Mr Projectionist!" shouted Danny at the top of his voice.

"Rolling!" replied the projectionist at the foot of his voice. The film was then projected on to Fatty's vast bulk, which was probably bigger than the original screen anyway! Luckily, for the sake of the story, he was wearing a white shirt.

18 "Great work, Danny!" cheered the crowd as they settled back to enjoy the film.

"Huh! That's the last time I suggest going to the pictures!" moaned Fatty, but since he was still eating, it sounded like, "Mumfle! Umfle! Gerble! Gloop!"

WELL, WELL, BELL!

NINE O'CLOCK—TIME THE KIDS WERE IN THE CLASSROOM.

CLANG CLANG

Much later—

FEEBLE CLANG

At the bell-maker's—

THAT'S THE BELL FOR US!

A GOOD CHOICE, YOUNG SIR, AND A REAL SNIP AT £14,999.99!

RUB

I'LL GET THE CASH.

CRASH

ER— WHICH BELL DO WE GET FOR 24p?

NOT TH_ ONE ANYW_

CLOSE

CLOSE

IT'S S-SOLIDLY BUILT T-TOO! TOO SOLIDLY FOR LITTLE ME TO C-CARRY.

COLLAPSE

BUT CLEVER LITTLE ME'S HAD A GOOD IDEA.

LEAP

IT C-CAN C-CARRY ME!

RUMBLE

HEY! IT DOESN'T HAVE A CLAPPER.

SO THAT'S WHY IT WAS SO CHEAP.

YIPPEE! WE'LL NEVER HEAR THE BELL— SO WE'LL NEVER HAVE TO COME TO SCHOOL!

WELL DO_E SMI_

NOT SO!

WH-WHERE ARE THEY?

Later still—

WHERE HAVE YOU LOT BEEN?

CLASS II B

THROB THROB

ARE WE LATE? WE DIDN'T HEAR THE BELL.

TAKE THE SCHOOL KITTY AND BUY A LOUDER BELL, SMIFFY.

WINSTON'S THE SCHOOL KITTY — THAT'S A PIGGY.

CLONK

Soon—

THIS ONE'S A BIT BATTERED, BUT IT WAS REALLY CHEAP.

STAGGER

WONDER WHY IT WAS SO CHEAP?

IT'S GOT A FEW CRACKS AND DENTS, BUT IT'S STILL A BARGAIN.

CEASE MAKING THOSE UNSEEMLY NOISES WITH YOUR TUM, BOY!

CHEEK! IT'S NOT ME!

TWANG

PING

LOUD RUMBLE

CRASH

AGH!

RUMBLE

TH-THE NEW BELL'S HERE!

I NOTICED!

STOMP

YOU WON'T HEAR THE BELL AT FOUR O'CLOCK— SO YOU'LL HAVE TO STAY IN HERE FOREVER!

WHAAAT?

SMIFFY

DONK

SCREECH TO HALT

I'M NOT SURE WH-WHO I AM, B-BUT MY FACE RINGS A B-BELL! HOW COME I GET ALL THE G-GOOD JOBS?

THERE'S THE FOUR O'CLOCK BELL— TIME FOR HOME!

BOINNNG

TUG

BOINNNG

GOOD CLEAN FUN!

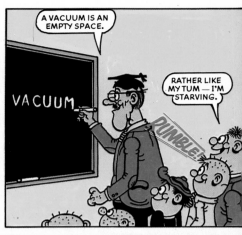

A VACUUM IS AN EMPTY SPACE.

RATHER LIKE MY TUM — I'M STARVING.

VACUUM

RUMBLE!

HELLO, MADAM — WE'RE SELLING THE WORLD'S FIRST MULTI-PURPOSE VACUUM CLEANER — IT CAN DO ABSOLUTELY ANYTHING!

I HOPE IT CAN GO AWAY, BECAUSE I DON'T WANT IT!

IT CAN WASH AND DRY WINDOWS IN SECONDS!

I SAID I DON'T WANT IT!

JAM!

WE'LL TRY SMUDGE'S HOUSE — HIS MUM'S ALWAYS CLEARING UP AFTER HIM.

HOW ABOUT A FREE DEMONSTRATION, MADAM?

OK — YOU CAN CLEAN SMUDGE'S ROOM?

So—

WHAT A SUPER CLEANER — I'LL BUY IT!

SEE YOU LATER, SMIFFY.

WHO SAYS I CAN'T DO ANYTHING RIGHT?

SMELL!

BOOM!

, TEACHER!

MEET MY OLD CHUM, ARTHUR DOILEY, CHILDREN.

CLASS IIB

ARTHUR SELLS VACUUM CLEANERS.

AND I'M LOOKING FOR DOOR-TO-DOOR SALESMEN.

THAT'S FOR US.

Later—

HAPPY SELLING, KIDS — I'M OFF TO SEE MY BANK MANAGER.

WE'LL TRY THIS DOOR FIRST.

GOODBYE!

OO!

Next door—

COULD WE INTEREST YOU IN THIS VACUUM CLEANER, SIR?

VACUUM CLEANER? COME INSIDE . . .

I WAS A VACUUM CLEANER SALESMAN MYSELF — THE ONLY WAY I COULD SELL THEM WAS TO BUY THEM ALL MYSELF.

HERE GOES!

ERK! THE CLEANER GOT LOST IN THE DIRT!

I'VE LOST THREE IN THERE ALREADY!

WE'LL TRY THIS EXTRA-STRONG CLEANER!

WATCH IT, SMIFFY — YOU NEARLY VACUUMED ME!

SORRY, SMUDGE!

! HE'S WRECKED IT!

WHY DIDN'T YOU EMPTY THE DUST BAG, SMIFFY?

I THOUGHT THE DUST WENT UP THE CABLE AND STRAIGHT INTO THE WALL.

OH, NO!

Back at school—

NOW SMIFFY'S HEAD'S A PERFECT VACUUM — TOTALLY EMPTY!

HAR-HAR!

HOLLOW THUNK!

. . . YOU GET LOADS OF VALENTINES.

I LOVE. . .

. .FIGHTING WITH YOU

OU SEND SHIVERS AND DOWN MY BACK.

WONDER WHICH ONE OF US TOOTS WILL SEND A VALENTINE TO?

MIRROR

GULP! WHAT IF SHE DOESN'T FANCY FAT BOYS?

INHALE

THERE — GOT THEM ON!

RHAPS TOOTS WON'T T FANCY SPOTS.

WHERE'S SPOTTY? CAN'T FIND HIM TO GIVE HIM SOMETHING.

GASP! SHE WANTS TO GIVE ME A CARD BUT SHE DOESN'T RECOGNISE ME.

FLESH COLOURED PAINT

HERE I AM! IT'S ME! ME! ME!

GOOD. I WANT TO GIVE YOU THIS.

GLUB.

SWOOSH

AH! HERE COMES MY SWEETHEART!

HIM? BUT WHAT DO YOU LIKE ABOUT WINSTON?

TO MY LITTLE FURRY DARLING

HE GIVES ME SUCH WONDERFUL PRESENTS!

SWOON

FOLLOW THE LEADER

I'M DANNY — I LEAD THE BASH STREET KIDS, BECAUSE I'M THE BEST.

I AM!

NO, ME!

I'M THE BEST!

JAB

BANG

BANG

BANG

BANG

BANG

THAT WAS A DRAW — THE INKY PELLET DUEL NOW

TWA

ANOTHER DRAW — THEY HAD THE SAME PLAN!

TRICK YO-YOING NEXT — GOOD IDEA, EH?

DONK

CLONK

Later —

MY POOR TEESH!

NEVER MIND THAT — THERE'S ONLY ONE WAY TO SETTLE THIS . . .

. . . FIGHT!

PUNCH

KICK

THUD

CEASE, AT ONCE!

ERK! YOU WERE MEANT TO WATCH FOR TEACHER, SMIFFY!

Just not Cricket!

LOOK AT THOSE TROPHIES.

I SEE NO TROPHIES.

BASH ST. CRICKET TROPHI...

WOW! LUCKY I'VE GOT PADS ON.

AGH! UNLUCKY...

BOUNCE

...I'M NOT PADDED IN OTHER PLACES. OOYAH!

ULP! THINK HE LEG-BROKE HIS GOOGLEY.

WAH!

SOME FIELDING PRACTICE NOW.

PONK!

EASY-PEASY!

OOPS!

WA...

SHATTER

EXACTLY! THAT'S WHY I WANT TO SEE IT FILLED THIS SEASON — TRAIN A TEAM OF WINNERS.

YES, YOUR MAGNIFICENCE!

BASH ST. CRICKET TROPHIES

TUG

So, in the dressing room —

PLEASE TRY TO WIN SOMETHING, OR I WON'T GET MY LITTLE PAY RISE.

LET'S TRAIN, TEAM!

THESE PADS ARE A BIT BIG!

LET'S SEE YOU BOWL ME OUT, 'ERBERT.

HE CAN'T SEE A THING!

BOP!

THUD!

YOU BLIND BAT — YOWP!

HERE'S MY LEG-GOOGLEY-BREAK WITH OVER THE SHOULDER, ROUND THE BEND, OFF SLICED, TWIZZLEY SILLY MID UP IN THE AIR.

ZOOM

I'VE GOT IT!

PHUNG!!

WE'VE HAD IT!

YOURS, SMIFFY!

THUD!

MUST SEE HOW MY WINNING TEAM IS SHAPING UP.

SIGH! MAYBE NEXT YEAR . . .

BASH ST. CRICKET TROPHIES

WATCH THIS SPACE

THE SOCKTOPUS

The silly Socktopus, I swear!
Has far less brains than fish have hair.
He has eight feet and, if you please,
He wears odd socks up to his knees.

Red ones, green ones, three in yellow –
He is a most peculiar fellow!
When I laughed he seemed to mind,
Saying, "Can't be helped – I'm colour blind!"

FEAR NOT, PUPILS! I'VE SOLD MY WATCH TO PAY OFF THE DEBT TO THE RAILWAY!

BOW ST.

WE'LL BE GLAD TO LEAVE THIS HORRIBLE TIME!

THERE WAS ENOUGH MONEY LEFT TO TRAVEL BACK FIRST CLASS!

VICTORIAN GRUB

SPLUDGE!

THAT GRAND LADY DOESN'T LOOK VERY AMUSED!

Off they go again!

1750
1650
1550
1450

TUG

And —

WE'VE ARRIVED IN THE YEAR 1250!

COO! A CASTLE!

ON GUARD, VARLET!

CLICK!

CLICK!

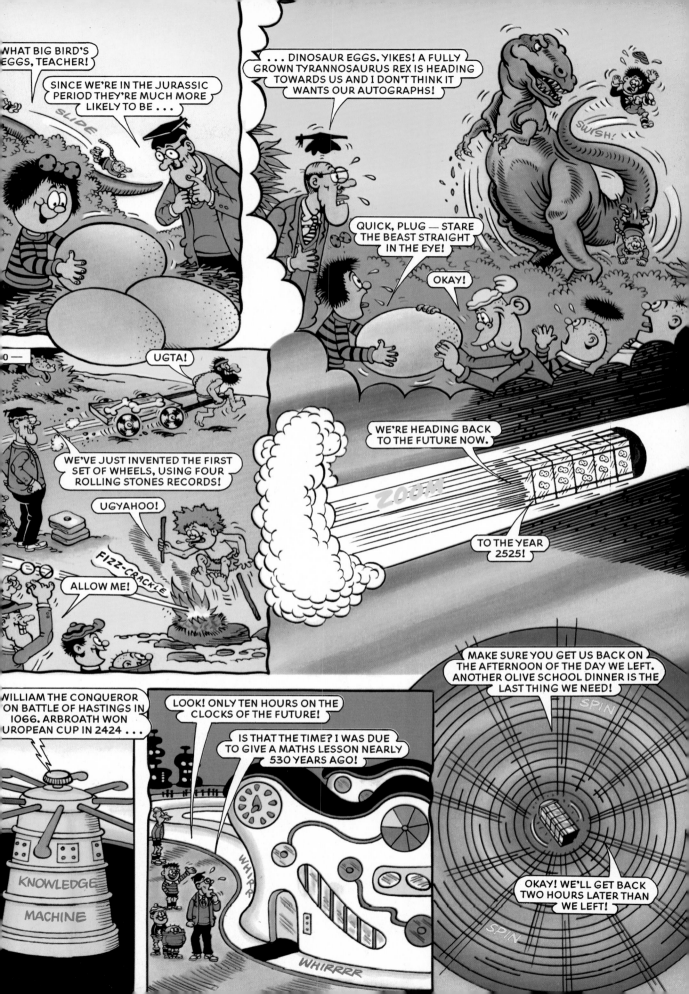

TO THE WOODS

I'M FED UP WITH SCHOOL.

ME, TOO!

ME — SMIFFY!

I'VE GOT A PLAN . . .

. . . LET'S RUN AWAY TO THE GREENWOOD AND BE OUTLAWS LIKE ROBIN HOOD!

NO! NO! IT WAS ONLY ME WHO WAS MEANT TO SWING!

ZOOM

ZOOM

ZOOM

OLD SCHOOL COOK

B-BAD P-PLAN!

WHUMP!

OLIVE SCHOOL COOK

OR ELSE — FIRE!

TWANG

PTCHEEE

TWANG

ZOOM

PTCHEEE

SPLUT!

YEEK!

DROP

GROAN! HAVE YOU LOT CONSIDERED GOING ON A DIET?

OOD PLAN!

In Bash Street Wood—

WE'LL ROB THE RICH AND GIVE TO THE POOR — WE'RE THE POOR!

GOOD PLAN!

SCALP

SMIFFY'S GOT IT WRONG AGAIN

I'LL SWING DOWN ON OUR VICTIM — THEN WE'LL HOLD HER TO RANSOM FOR SWEETS.

GOOD PLAN!

← OLIVE SCHOOL COOK

J-JUST AS WELL, MAYBE — THE HEAD WOULDN'T EVEN GIVE US A GOBSTOPPER TO GET OLIVE BACK!

DAZED

Later—

TEACHER SENT ME TO LOOK FOR THOSE NAUGHTY TRUANTS!

YOUR SWEETS — OR ELSE!

I DON'T HAVE ANY SWEETS! ER — OR ELSE WHAT?

PROD

SNIGGER!

N-NOT AT ME, TWITS! ANOTHER PLAN THAT DIDN'T WORK!

I'LL DIG A PIT FOR OUR NEXT VICTIM — YOU LOT GET BRANCHES TO COVER IT!

GOOD PLAN!

WE'VE GOT THE BRANCHES!

DIG

S PLAN DIDN'T ORK EITHER — OT ANOTHER?

YOU BET I HAVE . . .

SUCK

BEANO

. . . TEACHER! TEACHER, I SURRENDER!

HIDE AND SHRIEK

WE'RE EARLY — LET'S HAVE A GAME OF "HIDE AND SEEK TILL TEACHER ARRIVES.

GREAT IDEA.

BASH ST. SCHOOL

AND HERE'S PLUG.

GREAT AT COUNTING — HOPELESS AT SEEKING!

Soon—

I'M THE SEEKER NOW . . .

IF YOU WANT A JOB DONE PROPERLY, DO IT YOURSELF. 1, 2, 3, 4, 5, 6, 7, 8, 9 . . .

. . .10 — SMIFFY THINKS I CAN'T SEE HIM, BECAUSE HE CAN'T SEE ME!

SAND PIT

AND I JUST HAVE TO FOLLOW MY NOSE . . .

SNIFF!

. . .TO FIND FATTY.

DONG!

CLANG!

MEATY PIE NIFF

OOOOO!

SHAKE!

SNIGGER!

COUNT TO TEN THEN COME AND FIND US, SMIFFY.

OK! 1, 2 . . .

. . . ER — WHAT COMES AFTER 2?

GROAN! FORGET IT! WE NEED SOMEONE WHO CAN COUNT!

So—

. . . 8, 9, 10 — HERE I COME, READY OR NOT!

I SEE YOU, FATTY.

WONDER IF ANY OF THEM ARE HIDING INSIDE?

YEEK!

OH, NO — QUICK, EVERYBODY!

THIS ALWAYS HAPPENS WHEN PLUG SEES HIS REFLECTION WHEN HE DOESN'T EXPECT IT!

FAINT

E TRY, PLUG, BUT FORGOT YOUR EARS.

Then—

AHA!

GOT YOU, SPOTTY.

YANK

THUD!

OW!

CRUMP

rtly—

YOU'RE ALL USELESS AT HIDING!

NEVER MIND THAT! IT'S TIME FOR SOME VERY, VERY HARD SUMS.

GROAN! EVERY TIME I MENTION HARD SUMS THIS HAPPENS . . .

. . . I DON'T THINK THEY'RE USELESS AT HIDING AT ALL!

SNIFF!

TEACHER'S PET

...THE REST OF YOU ARE BOTTOM EQUAL — ALSO AS USUAL!

TITTER.

BE FRIENDLY WITH THE KIDS — MAYBE SOME OF YOUR GENIUS MAY RUB OFF ON THEM.

ANYTHING YOU SAY, SIR.

At the playing field—

LET'S PICK TEAMS FOR 5 A SIDE FOOTBALL — I PICK SMIFFY, TOOTS, SID AND ...

I PICK WILFRID, 'ERBERT, FATTY AND SPOTTY.

I'LL HAVE A WORD WITH THEM.

CUTHBERT MUST BE ALLOWED TO PLAY ...

AW, BUT ...

DUNK!

...OR ELSE EXTRA HOMEWORK!

OK — HE CAN JOIN THE GAME.

Soon—

STOP MOANING, CUTHBERT — WE'RE LETTING YOU JOIN THE GAME.

WHINE!

WILL WE GET DOWN?

NO WONDER YOU'RE BOTTOM OF THE CLASS! THROW SOMETHING UP TO DISLODGE IT, MORONS!

GREAT IDEA.

I DIDN'T MEAN MEEEEEE!

NOW CUTHBERT'S STUCK AS WELL, BUT I'VE GOT A SMASHING IDEA.

ME, TOO!

AND ME!

SO HAVE I!

ACK!

ERK! OUR WEIGHT WAS TOO MUCH FOR THE TREE!

Soon—

HOW'S MY PRIZE PUPIL DOING? ER — WHERE IS MY PRIZE PUPIL?

HEH-HEH! HE'S BOTTOM OF THE CLASS — FOR ONCE!

MOAN!

..SO YOU'RE ALL IN THE BASH STREET SEA CADETS.

NO WAY!

YOU'RE NOT ON — AND NEITHER ARE THESE UNIFORMS!

PLOP!

I'LL MAKE YOU EAT OLIVE'S DUMPLINGS — SHE MADE HER SPECIAL VINDALOO CABBAGE, PRUNE AND TRIPE ONES FOR TODAY.

OK — WE'LL JOIN — BUT FLARES ARE OUT OF FASHION!

THOSE ARE BELL-BOTTOMS, DUMB-BELL!

NO DEPTH-CHARGED BY SMIFFY.

GRR! WHAT WERE YOU DOING UP THERE?

I WAS IN THE CROW'S NEST BUT THE CROW OBJECTED!

NO WONDER, YOU HORRID OBJECT!

CAW!

I KNOW WHY THESE ARE CALLED BELL-BOTTOMS! THEY'RE ALL WRINGING WET!

SHAKE!

ENOUGH OLD JOKES — BOARD ANOTHER SHIP!

WE'LL START AGAIN — ROW!

BIG PUSH, KIDS.

NO! NO! THE OARS ARE TOO DEEP!

SPLUNGE!

PITY IT DIDN'T WORK!

YES, BRITAIN HAS A GREAT SEA-FARING HISTORY — WHICH IS LUCKY, BECAUSE . . .

. . . IT DOESN'T HAVE A GREAT SEA-FARING FUTURE WHEN THE KIDS GROW UP!

KEEP GOING — ANOTHER THREE MILLION BUCKETS SHOULD REFILL THE POND.

TAKING STEPS

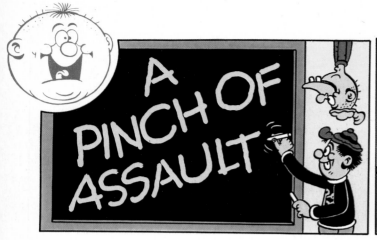

A PINCH OF ASSAULT

... WELL, CLEVER ME HAS MADE AN ASSAULT COURSE TO GET YOU FIT!

TH-THAT SOUNDS LIKE HARD WORK!

So —

READY, STEADY, GO!

BANG

ASSAULT COURSE

OVER THE BRIDGE FIRST.

ASSAULT COURSE

THROUGH THE PIPE!

DRAIN

ASSAULT COURSE →

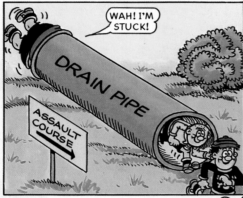

WAH! I'M STUCK!

DRAIN PIPE

ASSAULT COURSE →

GET ME OUT!

HELP!

DRAIN PIPE

THUD!

YOU WERE MEANT TO LET GO, TWIT!

I CAN DO THAT!

NO! NOT NOW! DON'T LET ...

SWING

SPLUDGE!

... TOO LATE!

TSK! THEY SHOULD HAVE BEEN BACK AGES AGO — WHERE ARE THEY?

THIS IS ALL YOUR FAULT — YOUR COURSE ASSAULTED US!

HELP!

WAH!

OW!

MUMBLE!

FAINT

DRAIN PIPE

OOH!

SID'S SILLY SEA WORLD!

BUBBLE PIPE

THE RED HERRING

The greatest detective was old Red Herring,
With a nose for a case that was quite unerring.
He'd track down thieves and vagabonds,
'Cross seas and lakes and garden ponds.

Once he tracked down down Killer Whale
And tried to drag him off to jail.
Just in time he had a hunch;
"I think that whale wants me for lunch!"

My first day at School

I was such a good-looking child even then!

Everyone thought so!

WOW! YOUR LOOKS COULD STOP TRAFFIC!

One woman couldn't contain herself!

She just HAD to show me off!

PLUG

WEIGHT FOR IT!

IT'S 9 O'CLOCK— INTO CLASS, CHILDREN.

GROAN!

EVERYONE PUSH!

TRUST TEACHER TO SPOIL THINGS!

Suddenly—

CRUMP!

OOF!

So—

WE'LL START WITH EXERCISE. WHAT ARE YOUR FAVOURITE EXERCISES, FATTY?

MY FAVOURITE'S CHEWING — CHOMP — CLOSELY FOLLOWED BY — GULP — SWALLOWING!

SIGH! IT'S NOT GOING TO BE EASY!

CURRY VINDALOO

TOUCHING TOES, BEGIN!

ERK! WHERE DID HE GO?

WHOOSH!

I WAS RIGHT!

HE BURST A WATER MAIN! HOW WILL WE GET HIM DOWN?

BY USING MY VAST BRAIN POWER!

WAH

SORRY! I SEEM TO BE STUCK!

YIPPEE! GOOD OLD FATTY! WE CAN'T GET IN — NO SCHOOL TODAY!

NOT SO FAST!

...NEW A LITTLE GENTLE ...ASION WOULD SOLVE IT!

...S THAT WHAT WE WERE DOING? I THOUGHT WE WERE PUSHING!

THE PROBLEM IS FATTY — HE'S GETTING TOO FAT!

CRACK!

SEE WHAT I MEAN? WE HAVE TO GET SOME OF FATTY'S WEIGHT OFF!

...CHING TOES? DON'T ...E DAFT! I HAVEN'T ...EN SEEN MY TOES FOR YEARS!

JOGGING WILL SOON GET SOME OF YOUR WEIGHT OFF — HUP, TWO, THREE . . .

OOPS!

WOW! I DIDN'T THINK YOU WERE SO HEAVY!

H-HOW CAN YOU THINK OF FOOD AT A TIME LIKE THIS?

RUMBLE

I DON'T THINK THAT'S FATTY'S TUM!

...OH, NO! TEACHER'S VAST BRAIN POWER'S NOT ...UITE AS VAST AS SMIFFY'S!

TEACHER DOESN'T WANT US TO GET SOME OF FATTY'S WEIGHT OFF NOW . . .

. . . HE WANTS US TO GET IT ALL OFF — OFF HIM! HA-HA!

DOH!

GASP!

HAPPY BIRTHDAY TO WHO?

HAPPY BIRTHDAY TO YOU, HAP... BIRTHDAY TO YOU, HAPPY...

OOH!

CLASS IIB

IT IS. AND WE'VE ARRANGED A SURPRISE PARTY FOR YOU, SMIFFY. HOW OLD ARE YOU NOW?

LET ME THINK...

WELL, WHAT'S YOUR AGE?

X + Y 2

TRYING TO PLAY THIS CHAIR, BUT IT ISN'T VERY MUSICAL.

CLUNK!

"PIN THE TAIL ON THE DONKEY" WILL BE MUCH SAFER.

SPIN!

AGHH

SLURP!

BLAST!

SNIGGER! MY WISH CAME TRUE ANYWAY! BURP — PARDON!

ROTTEN GLUTTON! YOU'VE SCOFFED OUR SHARE AS WELL! PREPARE TO BE BASHED!

... BIRTHDAY DEAR ...

... ER — WHOSE BIRTHDAY IS IT?

IT'S YOUR BIRTHDAY, TWIT!

IT IS? OH, BOY!

BLAST!

GOT IT — OLDER THAN LAST YEAR — THAT'S WHAT IT IS!

GROAN! FORGET IT — WE'LL PLAY "MUSICAL CHAIRS"!

PULL!

WH-WHAT ARE YOU D-DOING, SMIFFY?

FRANTIC BLOWING

HOW DID I DO?

OOOO!

NICE TRY — WRONG DONKEY!

OUCH! ENOUGH GAMES — WE'LL HAVE THE CAKE INSTEAD.

PLUCK!

So —

BLOW OUT THE CANDLE AND MAKE A WISH, SMIFFY.

MIGHTY SUCK OF AIR

LET ME AT IT!

CEASE THIS FIGHTING BEFORE SOMEONE GETS HURT ...

HUD! BOP!

... N-NAMELY MEEEE!

THUMP! BIFF!

In hospital —

GROAN! SMIFFY'S BIRTHDAY HAS PUT YEARS ON ME!

MEDICINE

BANGERS and CRASH

GROAN! SCHOOL AGAIN!

AND WE'RE GOING TO BE LATE AGAIN.

So, at 9.23 —

THIS LATENESS HAS TO CEASE, STOP AND DESIST — OR ELSE! NINE O'CLOCK IS STARTING TIME.

SCRUB!

Next morning —

I'M NOT GOING TO BE LATE TODAY — I HAVE TRANSPORT.

ZOOM

WOWF!

CRUNCH!

YIKES EVERYONE HAS THE SAME IDEA.

TEACHER'S PARKING SPACE

ZOOM

CRUMP!

GROAN! TH-THERE G-GOES OUR TRANSPORT.

I GET TO DRIVE, BECAUSE I'M THE TEACHER — LET'S HAVE A TRIAL RUN.

I WANT TO BE ON TOP!

ME TOO!

GLUB!

TEACHER'S ALWAYS ON TIME BECAUSE HE'S GOT TRANSPORT — EVEN IF IT IS A BANGER.

BANG!

HIS BANGER'S JUST GONE BANG FOR THE LAST TIME. HE'LL BE LATE AS WELL.

WRAP UP, LITTLE BROTHER — MY NEED IS GREATER THAN YOURS!

WHIZZ

MUCH MORE HEALTHY THAN A CAR — I'M USING LEAD-FREE SHOES!

VOOM

I'M EARLY AND TEACHER'S PARKING SPACE IS JUST RIGHT FOR MY CARTIE.

TEACHER'S PARKING SPACE

I'VE AN IDEA, BECAUSE I'M A CLEVER TEACHER.

In the woodwork class —

. . . THAT BIT THERE GOES . . .

THUD

PLANS

Much later —

WHAT A FINE VEHICLE. THERE'S ROOM FOR ALL OF US ABOARD.

BEING ON THE BOTTOM'S FOR SAPS!

CREAK!

YOU CAN'T ALL BE ON T-TOP OR THIS THING MIGHT . . .

. . . COLLAPSE! ARGH!

GROAN! THIS IS ONE FORM OF TRANSPORT WE COULD HAVE DONE WITHOUT.

AMBULANCE

GROAN! MOAN!

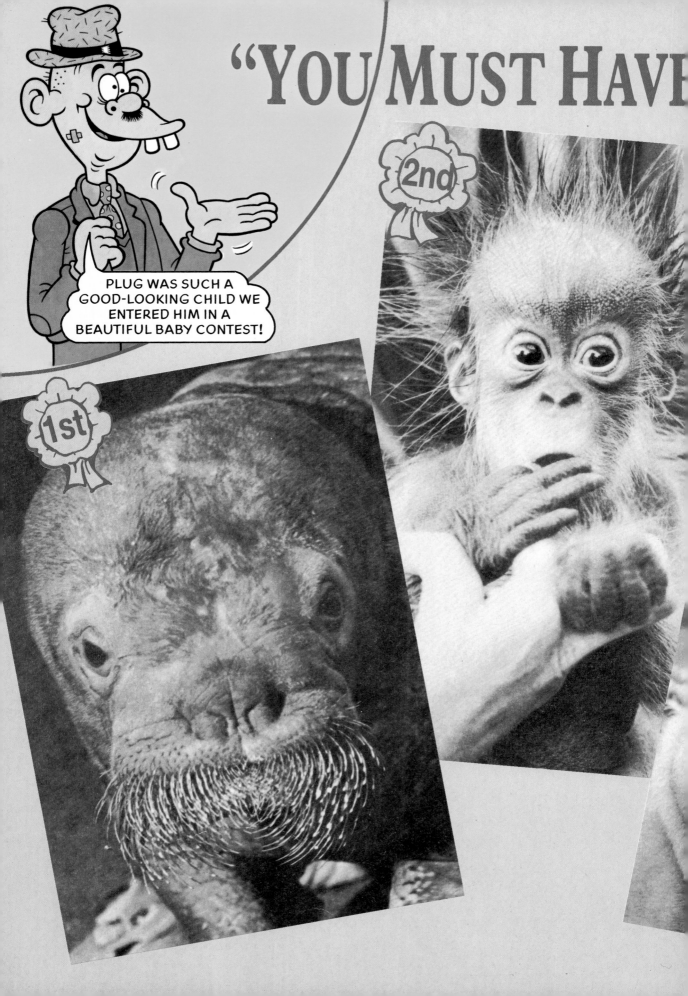

AGH!

ZOOM!

AGHAGAIN!

DOING! DOING!

ZOOM!

FLATTEN!

F-FROM TH-THE KIDS' F-FOOTBALL G-GAME— TH-THAT'S WHERE!

OU'RE THE BIGGEST LY — SO OFF YOU GO!

EEK! A BULLY-OFF'S LIKE A KICK OFF IN FOOTBALL— I DIDN'T MEAN THROW A BULLY OFF!

WACK!

THUD!

At the ice rink—

FIGURE SKATING IS A GENTLE SPORT — BEGIN!

GLIDE!

TUMBLE!

OH, NO!

SLIDE!

SLIP!

SLIP!

. . CHARGE!

W-WAIT!

SHOVE!

SNAP!

EEK!

SHUDDER!

SHAKE!

WHUMP!

G-GUESS WHAT? WE C-CAUGHT THE STEEPLE!

DAZED!

DAZED!

GROAN! IDIOTIC IDIOTS! STEEPLE-CHASING DOESN'T MEAN YOU MUST CHASE A THING THAT DOESN'T MOVE!

WELL, I WISH YOU'D SAY WHAT YOU MEAN AND MEAN WHAT YOU SAY!

WHAAAAT?

REMEMBER TEACHER SAID THAT BIG WORD?

YOU MEAN . . .

. . . SPIFFLICATION?

THAT'S THE ONE! WELL, I THINK HE MEANT IT!

SWISH!

EVERYONE TO THE COURTS — I'M GOING TO TEACH YOU TENNIS.

GREAT!

OK, SMIFFY — TRY A SERVICE.

BACK IN A MINUTE.

ZOOM!

LUNCHEON IS SERVED!

NOT WAITER SERVICE, TWIT — CAN'T YOU DO ANYTHING RIGHT?

WACK

YOU WERE FACING THE WRONG WAY, YOU SHORT-SIGHTED OAF!

THUD THUD

WHO SAID THAT?

SID, YOU SERVE TO PLUG.

OK!

...YES! HOO-HA-HARDY-HAR-HA!

SHLUP!

LAUGH THIS OFF, CHUCKLING CHAPPY!

WAH!

FOUL!

MEEMAWMEEMAW!

TENNIS COURT

POLICE

POLICE

FLATTEN

EVERYONE TO THE COURTS — WE'RE GOING TO TEACH YOU ABOUT LAW AND ORDER!

TAP

PROD

THUD

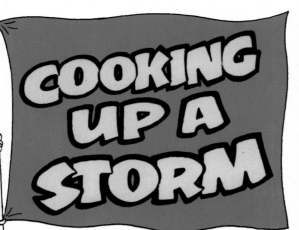

COOKING UP A STORM

ANY COMPLAINTS ABOUT THE FOOD?

SCHOOL DINING HALL

NNNNGH!

TUG

OOPSH! I SHEE WHAT YOU MEAN, PLUG.

SHLOOP!

BITE!

OW!

AND WHA ABOUT TH

YOU'VE GOT TO GET OLIVE TO IMPROVE HER COOKING!

BUT I DON'T WANT TO HURT H-HER FEELINGS.

I'D . . . ER — LIKE TO PRESENT YOU WITH THIS COOKERY BOOK.

ARE YOU SAYING I'M A BAD COOK?

COOKERY BOOK

THUD!

N-NO! YOU'RE THE BEST COO IN THE SCHOOL

SHE'S THE ONLY COOK IN THE SCHOOL!

COOKERY BOOK

PAT

YIKES! I'M NOT TOUCHING THAT TILL ONE MUG — ER — BRAVE VOLUNTEER TESTS IT FIRST!

BOOM!

So —

ROTTEN LOT! I NEVER VOLUNTEERED! GAGHH!

YES!

THIS SOUP'S COLD!

ARE YOU SURE?

OF COURSE I'M FLAMING SURE!

OUCH! A SCOTCH BROTH ICE-LOLLY!

— THUD! WHAP!

THIS PIZZA'S TOUGH!

LET ME TRY.

THROB!

LOOKS LIKE A PERFECTLY GOOD DUMPLING TO ME.

IT'S NOT A DUMPLING — IT'S GRAVY!

RUMBLE!

EVEN THE BREAD'S TOO HARD . . .

GLUMPH!

WHAP!

WOW! MY TEETH WOULD HAVE BEEN BROKEN — IF I'D HAD THEM IN MY MOUTH!

'S ALL RIGHT — I'LL MAKE SOMETHING E FROM IT.

PEPPER-POT STILL UP THERE

Then —

ACHOOO! PESKY PEPPER!

PEPPER

BOKERY BOOK

NOW HOW DOES THIS RECIPE GO? TWO SHOVELS OF CURRY POWDER . . .

CAN'T SEE WITHOUT HER SPECS

Soon —

I'VE MADE ANOTHER LUNCH FOR YOU LOT!

HOW WAS IT?

VERY NICE! VERY . . .

. . . HOT! BURP! PARDON ME!

Soon —

THREE CHEERS FOR THE BEST COOK IN BASH STREET SCHOOL — OR SHE WOULD BE — IF THERE WAS ANY SCHOOL LEFT!

SCHOOL

THE TURTLE DOVE

The Turtle Dove will do your brain,
Her singing's like a blocked up drain.
She sang and sang all afternoon
In Sammy Shark's coral saloon.

Her voice it carried 'cross the reef –
A noise like scraping nails on teeth.
At times like this it's just as well,
She can retreat inside her shell!

My first day at School

Mum gave me a big breakfast.

And a playtime snack and packed lunch to take with me.

School was hard to get into.

The other kids liked me straight away.

I'm not so sure about Teacher, though!

FATTY

AN INSPECTOR CALLS

THE SCHOOL INSPECTOR'S COMING TOMORROW.

NO PROBLEM! MY CLASS IS PRETTY BRIGHT...

SNAP!

DIARY

NO, TWIT — I AM SMIFFY!

I AM STUFFY

YOU ARE? THEN WHO AM I?

GROAN! FORGET WRITING!

TWIST!

KICK!

WE COULD TRY LANGUAGES. SAY SOMETHING IN FRENCH.

TOO EASY...

TAP! TAP!

...SOMETHING IN FRENCH! SEE? WORD PERFECT!

I KNEW IT — HIS BRAIN'S NOT EVEN WORKING ON BOTH CELLS!

IF YOU'RE NOT GOOD AT ART, I'M SUNK!

I'LL PAINT YOU.

PAINT BOX

SNAP SHUT!

Soon—

WHERE AM I?

INSIDE THE HOUSE — I CAN'T PAINT PEOPLE!

SLOW TO FLOO

...APART FROM SMIFFY!

RIP!

NIC CKEN →

THERE, THERE — JUST SHOW THE INSPECTOR ALL THE THINGS SMIFFY'S GOOD AT.

I'M DOOMED — DOOMED!

THUD! THUD!

CLAS II B

So—

I WANT TO FIND WHAT YOU'RE GOOD AT, SMIFFY WRITE YOUR NAME.

DAZZLE!

TRY ARITHMETIC — YOU'VE GOT TWO APPLES AND FATTY TAKES ONE...

ICE CUBES

WORRY BEADS

WHAT HAVE YOU DONE WITH MY APPLE, YOU ROTTEN FATTY?

YAWN!

ARITHMETIC'S OUT!

LET ME AT THE PIPPIN-PINCHER!

TUG!

TUG!

THERE MUST BE SOMETHING YOU'RE GOOD AT — WHAT ABOUT FOOTBALL?

LET'S SEE...

ZLE!

SCRATCH!

...NO, MY FOOT'S NOT EVEN WHISPERING — NEVER MIND BAWLING!

TWANG!

THUD!

BAWL! BOO-HOO! WHEN THE INSPECTOR SEES YOU, I'LL GET SACKED! WHINE!

THAT'S IT — YOU'RE GOOD FOR NOTHING — I'M SUNK!

E!

SWOOSH!

Next day—

NO, I'M NOT — I'M SAVED — BECAUSE THERE IS ONE THING SMIFFY'S GOOD AT...

'MORNING!

SCHOOL

SCHOOLS INSPECTOR

...FORGETTING TO COME TO SCHOOL!

EXAM TIME!

GROAN!

NO! I'LL TAKE THESE — DON'T MISUSE SCHOOL EQUIPMENT OR IT WON'T WORK!

SNATCH

BAH! I'VE GOT A SPLINTER IN MY FINGER!

THROB

TO THE HOSPITAL!

ERK! NO! IT'S ALL RIGHT!

CLASS IIB

PUSH

So—

SORRY, BUT I COULDN'T HELP HURTING MY BIG TOE!

ZOOM

WE'VE GOT TO STOP, TEACHER DUCKS CROSSING!

QUACK MARCH!

SWIVEL

THUD

KICK

YOU'LL BE SAFER NOW . . .

DAZED

TSK! WHAT ARE YOU HANGING ABOUT THERE FOR?

MEEMAWMEEMAW!

BASH ST HOSPITAL

ZOOM

WAY IN

ZONK!

In Ward 9—

WHAT ARE YOU IN FOR, MATE?

I GOT A SPLINTER IN MY FINGER!

HOMEWORK JITTERS

OK, LET ME HAVE YOUR HOMEWORK BOOKS.

HEY! THIS IS ALL STICKY, SPOTTY.

I KNOW — ALL THE PAGES FELL OUT . .

I'LL BE SAFE IN HERE!

BASH ST. POND

BZZZ!

PRANG!

BASH ST. POND

OOYAH!

AGH!

OO!

I WOULD HAVE BEEN ALL SAFE, IF THE POND HAD BEEN DEEPER!

AT LEAST IT'S DRIED ME OFF.

SINGE!

DOESN'T ANYONE HAVE NICE, NORMAL HOMEWORK?

YESSIR! MESIR! HOMEWORK ALL NEATLY DONE AND IT'S . . .

. . . HOWLLL!

SIGH! NOW I'M ALL WET AGAIN!

SMIFFY, YOU'VE DONE YOUR HOMEWORK, HAVEN'T YOU?

WELL, I WAS GOING TO — I WOULD HAVE DONE — ONLY . . .

WRING!

My first day at School

I took my pets with me on my first day.

I had to leave them at the gate.

My pets were lost without me.

DIG! DIG! DIG! DIG! DIG! DIG!

They couldn't wait to see me!

And my new pals couldn't wait to meet them!

COME BACK AT ONCE!

SIDNEY

DOPE TEST

TO SCHOOL

LOOK . . .

. . . ER, WHAT'S MY NAME AGAIN?

WHAT A SCREAM — HE'S THE FUNNIEST KID!

CAN'T HAVE THIS!

So —

HERE'S WHAT WE'LL DO . . .

STOMP

AW, COME ON — LET ME IN ON THE SECRET, PALS.

SECRET MEETING IN PROGRESS

In school —

ROLL CALL, FIRST — ARE YOU HERE SMIFFY?

WELL, IF THAT'S THE WAY YOU WANT TO PLAY — WE'LL DO SOME SUMS!

REALLY MAD →

RIP

WHAT'S 24 PLUS 3, SMIFFY?

5

16

9

2

. . . 36, 27 — THE ANSWER IS MAYBE!

OO! EEK! ARGH!

PLUCK

TWING

FORGET SUMS — WHERE ARE THE HIMALAYAS?

CAN'T FIND THEM ANYWHERE!

NOPE!

... WE WANT OUR AUTOGRAPH BOOKS SIGNED.

OK!

STEADY ON — WE'LL SIGN ALL — WHERE DID THEY GO?

TRAMPLE

YOU'RE OUR FAVOURITE BECAUSE YOU'RE SO SILLY — SIGN, PLEASE.

BEST WISHES FROM ...

YES

BLAST

BLAST

BLAST

YIKES! I'M SEEING THINGS — A WHOLE CLASS OF SMIFFIES!

SMIFFY MASKS

... 19, 20 — OOPS! WE'VE RUN OUT OF THINGS TO COUNT ON!

DONK

92

46

3

T HERE!

IF EVER A TEACHER SUFFERED ...

WHAT ARE WE GOING TO DO NOW?

I KNOW WHAT I'M GOING TO DO NOW ...

... I AM GOING TO GO BANANAS!

BLOW

WHERE DID ET ALL THAT LY MONEY?

THEY ONLY COST 50 PENCE AT THE SUPERMARKET.

BAH! THEY'RE USELESS CHOCOLATE COINS!

BITE

I WOULDN'T SAY THEY WERE USELESS!

CHOMP!

SILVER PAPER'S NOT SO NICE THOUGH.

LET'S GO CAROL-SINGING TO RAISE CASH.

TWANG!

WASTE PAPER

WISH YOU A MERRY CHRISTMAS, WISH YOU A MERRY CHRISTMAS, WISH YOU A MERRY CHRISTMAS, AND A HAPPY NEW YEAR.

SCREECH!

HOWL!

GRR! YOUR AWFUL WAILING'S WAKENED THE BABY, TERRIFIED THE CAT AND WORSE — WE COULDN'T HEAR NEIGHBOURS!

BAWL!

RIP!

RIP!

GOOD KING WHATSISNAME LOOKED OUT, ON THE FEAST OF THINGYMABOB . . .

SQUEAK!

SQUEAL!

GORDON ZOLA'S CHEESE FACTORY

WELL DONE, KIDS — YOU'VE SCARED ALL THE MICE AWAY WITH YOUR SINGING!

CHEESY NIFF

So —

FOR YOU, DEAR TEACHER.

OOOOOH, TA MUCHLY.

BOW

THE KIDS BEING NICE? I MIGHT HAVE GUESSED!

TICKET TO SIBERIA
ONE WAY